Sugar High, Sugar High, Sugar Low, Sugar Low

Dr. Maya Lebow

Illustrations: A. Isenberg

Published by
Targum Publishers
Shlomo ben Yosef 131a/1
Jerusalem 9380581
editor@targumpublishers.com

Illustrations and graphic layout by:
Adina.Isenberg8@gmail.com

Distributed by
Ktav Publishers & Distributors Inc.
527 Empire Blvd.
Brooklyn, NY 11225-3121
Tel: 718-972-5449, 201-963-9524
Fax: 718-972-6307, 201-963-0102
www.ktav.com
Printed in Israel

Ackn♡wledgements

I would like to first thank my husband, YDL, for his encouragement and motivational nudges to use my creativity to write a children's book,

Natan Chaim, my energetic, one-of-a-kind, first- born, and true inspiration for this work,

Eliyahu, M♡ttie, Yankel, and Racheli always a ready audience for eema's outrageous stories,

my two sisters, Hadar, logistical girl Friday, and Orit, the cheerleader for rooting me on,

my parents Han♡ch and Pnina Aizenman for their generous support always,

Dr. Yael Kuperman, for her enthusiasm and nutritional advice,

Chanie Green for being a true sounding board always, and

Dr. Elaine Adler for her linguistic magic.

A birthday celebration in school, a time for sweets.
Miri generously hands out treats.
Shoshi grabs one toffee, two toffees, and just a few more.
There's no point in leaving behind anymore.
With Shoshi's pockets full, school is over.
She'll just pop a few more as her house gets closer.

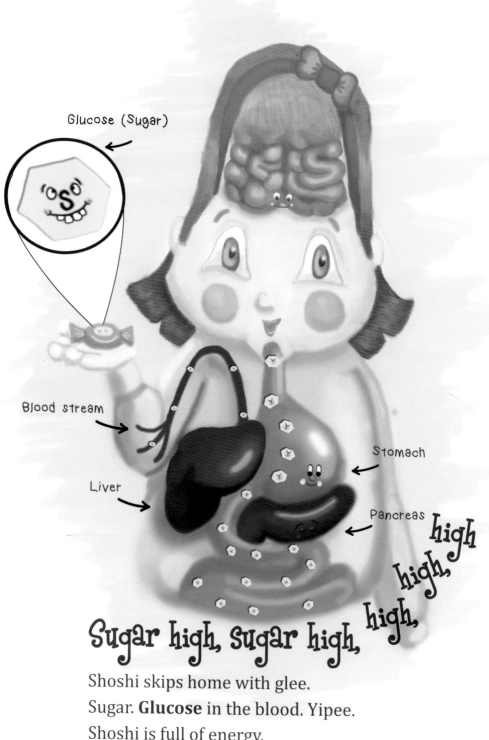

Glucose (Sugar)

Blood stream

Liver

Stomach

Pancreas

high high, high, high,

Sugar high, sugar high,

Shoshi skips home with glee.
Sugar. **Glucose** in the blood. Yipee.
Shoshi is full of energy.
Brain's **hypothalamus** gets the signal,
   we are satisfied.
No need to rush, the stomach is gratified.

Shoshi's glucose levels are rising, but our
     body does not need such amounts.
Too much can make us forget our good
     middos, which is what really counts.
Beta cells in the **pancreas** are now
     pumping **insulin** all around,
working hard trying to remove all the glucose found.

The insulin spreads to all her muscles
     so that they won't tire.
Soon, Shoshi starts to perspire.
Insulin is now high, and glucose has run dry.
The motor is running, the tank is on empty. Sigh.

Sugar low, sugar low, low

low,

low

Shoshi gets home. Her mood has soured.
Her muscles feel like they can't be powered.
Glucose is not high as it was in school.
Shoshi begins to lash out like a fool.
Mommy asks her to pick up the toys.
Instead she refuses without any poise.
"Mottie and Racheli made the mess here on the floor.
They should pick them up as their chore."

Mommy sends Shoshi to her room.
Shoshi can't focus on math homework in her gloom.
Her stomach is also grumbling a noisy tune.

The morning sun rises with promise.
    Shoshi rushes downstairs.
As she swipes the sugar flares,
Eliyahu and Mottie give her glares.
Mommy says "No, no, no!" to so much sugar.
    "Try a warm bowl of oatmeal,"
    Mommy offers to appease.
Shoshi feels the sting, says "thanks,
    pass the blueberries, please."

Sugar **high**, not too **high**,
Sugar LOW, not too LOW,

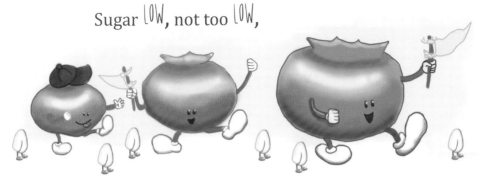

Shoshi is on her way with
SUGAR levels STEADY IN T♥W.
She scoots out the door, kiss to Mommy.
A new day to keep sugar from causing her brain to go astray.

Recess outside, Miri offers Shoshi a lolly.
    Shoshi, full of temptation,
places her tuna sandwich back in
    the bag without hesitation.
Lick, lick her tongue wags.

Morah Spitzer calls the class back to order.
Shoshi sits down to listen,
but her blood is in transition.
She whispers to Miri, she wants another treat.
Shoshi's foot is even tapping to an unheard beat.

Morah hisses and shushes.
Hoshi heeds and blushes.
The math problems continue on,
but insulin is rising. The glucose is gone.
Hoshi feels beaten.
Too bad the tuna is still uneaten.

Sugar low, sugar low, low, low, low,

Not so many moments pass,
a thirst sensation is creeping up in mass.
Rivki removes a pink pen. Shoshi is absolutely aghast.
She declares to Rivki that she is the rightful owner.

In the meantime, Morah Spitzer hovers in the corner.
Chumash stopped, the parshah lesson is over.
Oblivious, Shoshi grabs the pen, butts
    Rivki with her shoulder.
Shoshi is now on the way to the principal
    carrying a huge boulder.

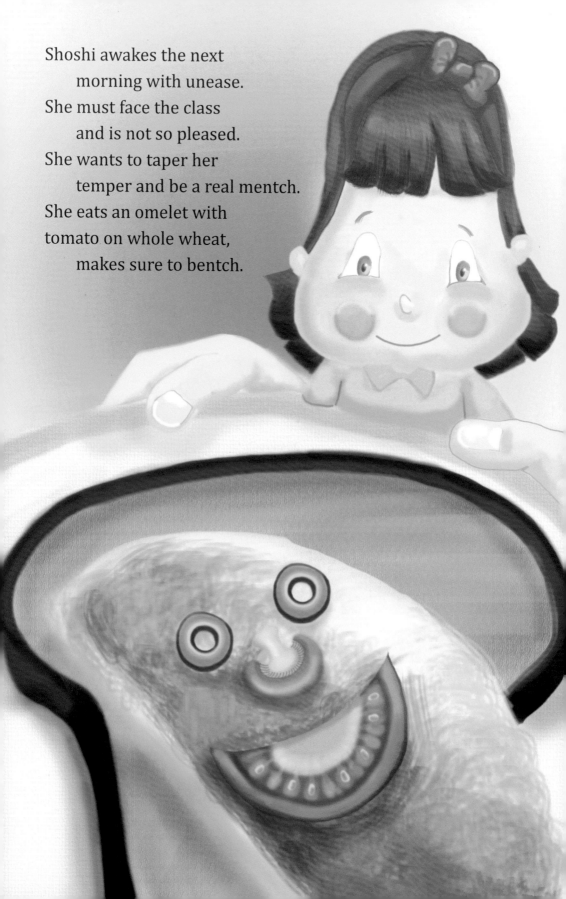

Shoshi awakes the next
    morning with unease.
She must face the class
    and is not so pleased.
She wants to taper her
    temper and be a real mentch.
She eats an omelet with
tomato on whole wheat,
    makes sure to bentch.

Sugar **high,** not too **high,**
Sugar LOW, not too LOW,
Shoshi is on her way with
SUGAR lEVElS STEAdy IN TOW.

Off to school, the sun is surreal.
Morah Spitzer, explains the
long division with zeal.

Breaktime, Miri downs gummy candies and a coke.
Shoshi today won't choke.
She finishes a yogurt in the breeze.
Time for chumash, and even parshah passes with ease.

Sugar **high**, not too **high**,
Sugar LOW, not too LOW,
Shoshi is on her way with
SUGAR levels steady in tow.

Shoshi gets home with impeccable timing.
Her legs rush her to Mommy and her eyes shining.
She exclaims about the pop quiz, but Mommy already knows.
Morah Spitzer called to gush on Shoshi's bright day
     without a tale of woes.
Shoshi sat still, paid attention;
her brain and body were not in tension.
With enough glucose fueling her thoughts,
the insulin did not disrupt with its interfering plots.

Shoshi nibbles on an almond as Mommy
        prepares a salmon salad.
Meanwhile, Yanky pounds on the floor with a teary ballad.
For one more wafer,
Mommy has learned to not waiver.

Yanky's sugar is LOW, LOW, LOW,

and Mommy knows,
Soon, he will eat and stop fighting with blows.

As Mommy keeps trying to show, if you
    drop the sweets and start eating right,
Hashem will keep our bodies with enough
    might for our brains to learn and feel alright.

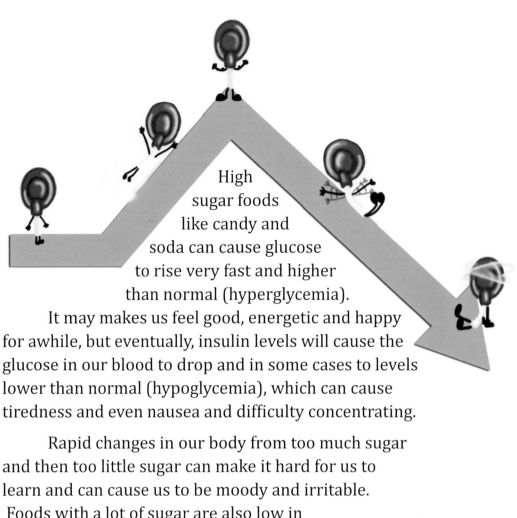

High sugar foods like candy and soda can cause glucose to rise very fast and higher than normal (hyperglycemia). It may makes us feel good, energetic and happy for awhile, but eventually, insulin levels will cause the glucose in our blood to drop and in some cases to levels lower than normal (hypoglycemia), which can cause tiredness and even nausea and difficulty concentrating.

Rapid changes in our body from too much sugar and then too little sugar can make it hard for us to learn and can cause us to be moody and irritable. Foods with a lot of sugar are also low in vitamins like B6, B9, and B12 and low amounts can also cause our moods to sour.

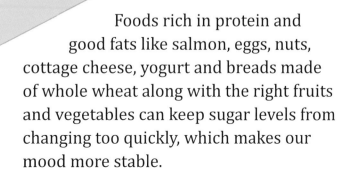

Foods rich in protein and good fats like salmon, eggs, nuts, cottage cheese, yogurt and breads made of whole wheat along with the right fruits and vegetables can keep sugar levels from changing too quickly, which makes our mood more stable.

Insulin
Beta Cells

KEYW♡RDS:

GLUC♡SE is a type of sugar. Our body converts the sugar we eat from candy and sodas as well as complex carbohydrates like bread, pasta or potatoes, to glucose. Glucose is sent to our brain and muscles. It provides us with the energy for every task from running to learning new topics in school.

HYP♡THALAMUS is a part of the brain. The hypothalamus tells our body when we are full (satiated) or hungry since it is able to sense how much glucose and other nutrients are left circulating in the blood.

BETA CELLS are a special type of cell found in the pancreas that produce insulin.

PANCREAS is an organ in our body that has cells that release insulin into the blood.

INSULIN is a protein released from the pancreas when the body senses the blood sugar is elevated.

DIABETES TYPE 2 is a chronic state of high blood sugar in which our body does not produce enough insulin and therefore does not lower blood sugar levels well anymore. This is dangerous and can cause damage to blood vessels and cells in the brain and body. This medical condition can be controlled through by cutting back on sugar, exercising, and in some people receiving shots of insulin.

DIABETES TYPE 1 is a state of high blood sugar, which occurs due to the body's inability to produce insulin. This usually happens when the beta cells in the pancreas are mistakenly destroyed by the body's immune system. People with type 1 diabetes need to inject insulin according to the amount of carbohydrates they eat.